Christmas Elves

Being Themselves

Author: Yolanda T. Marshall
Illustrator: Daria Lavrova
© 2022 Chalkboard Publishing Inc
ISBN: 978-1-77105-793-6

Published by Chalkboard Publishing Inc

Canada This project is funded in part by the Government of Canada.

May all the children around the world feel loved and celebrated, whether they are naughty or nice. **Happy Holidays!**

"Twas the night before Christmas."

Santa reads a story from his picture book,
As the naughty elves served a mischievous look
"I know that stare, so don't you dare."
"Be nice this year; Christmas season is here!"

The elves delight in being Santa's helpers.
Some even enjoy being Christmas pranksters.
They do naughty things most children wouldn't dare,
Like hiding Santa's hat, boots, and underwear.

"Oh no! That's not my style! I must be me!
A rare elf of glorious royalty!"

I'm excited about treating myself,
To tasty cookies while I sit on a shelf.
Black cake cookies and other festive munches
For my breakfasts, dinners, and even lunches!

All that holiday sugar won't work for me.
You see, I prefer lots of fruits and veggies.
Pears, carrots, apples, spinach, and celery.
I'll create all the candy canes sugar-free!

Although I enjoy creating holiday joy,
I must travel before crafting one more toy.
It's time to leave for my vacation fun,
Out of the cold snow, into the warm sun!

It's the jolly time of year to feed my curiosity,
A world of Christmas traditions for me to learn and to see.
I'll watch diverse families celebrate and just be themselves,
And take notes to share with Santa as I sit on their shelves.

Junkanoo
Bahamas

I'm the most adventurous elf of them all,
Sneaking into the sleigh before it's nightfall.
I hope that Santa doesn't see me,
Climbing and sliding down the chimney.

Santa always encourages the little elves
To be their unique and merriest selves.
He welcomes their differences with love.
Even when they hide his Christmas gloves!

COCONUT SUGAR CAKES

INGREDIENTS:

- 2 cups granulated sugar
- ⅔ cups water
- 1 tbsp minced fresh ginger (or ¼ tsp dried ginger powder)

- 2 cups unsweetened desiccated coconut
- ½ tsp mixed essence or vanilla extract
- ¼ tsp salt
- 6–8 drops red or green food colouring (optional)

METHOD:

1. Line a baking sheet with parchment paper.

2. In a medium, heavy saucepan over medium-high heat, combine the sugar, water, and ginger.

3. Bring to a boil, stirring often until the sugar dissolves and the mixture thickens into a light syrup (about 8–10 minutes).

4. Reduce the heat to low, and add the dried coconut, mixed essence (or vanilla), and salt. Mix well. Continue to cook for 2–3 minutes, stirring frequently. Remove from heat.

5. Working quickly, drop a mound of 2 tbsps of the mixture onto the lined baking sheet. Flatten it slightly with a wet spoon to form a small cake. Continue until half the coconut mixture has been formed into cakes.

6. For the remaining half of the coconut mixture, stir in a few drops of your choice of food colouring. Mix until your desired colour is reached.

7. Form the tinted mixture into small cakes on the lined baking sheet.

8. Allow to cool and harden for 15–20 minutes before serving.

"Dear readers, cooking as a family creates special memories. Here is a recipe by a good friend of mine, Monique Creary, Educator and Owner/Culinary Instructor of Now You're Cooking. Please remember, there should always be an adult present when children are participating in cooking activities."

- Yolanda T. Marshall

Did you know?

In **Germany** and **Austria**, kids and teens sing carols at families' doorsteps during Christmas. This is their Sternsinger tradition.

In **Mexico**, Las Posadas is a Mexican Christmas Christian tradition celebrated between December 16th and December 24th. The celebration includes cultural foods and drinks, sweet treats, music, and piñatas.

In **China**, some families offer Peace Apples as gifts on Christmas Eve. It is a gift-giving tradition.

In **The Bahamas**, Junkanoo is an African-Caribbean Christmas tradition celebrating the holidays with masqueraders dancing, music, and cultural costumes. In Jamaica, it is referred to as "Jonkonnu."

Activities Page

Draw a picture of yourself as an Elf.

Draw a picture of Santa Claus.

Tell us, what are your favourite candies, cookies, and vegetables?

If you celebrate the holidays, share some of your seasonal traditions.

If you don't celebrate the holidays, share your favourite festivities.

Look into a mirror and say, **"I love myself!"**